The
FIRST FIVE YEARS
A Child's Record Book and Keepsake

Caroline Ash

DORLING KINDERSLEY

LONDON • NEW YORK • SYDNEY • MOSCOW

A DORLING KINDERSLEY BOOK

Design Bernard Higton

Editor Lorraine Turner
Senior Managing Editor Krystyna Mayer
Deputy Art Director Carole Ash
DTP Designer Bridget Roseberry
Production Sarah Coltman

Photography
Dorling Kindersley would like to thank the following for
the photographs appearing in the book:
Paul Bricknell, Martin Brigdale, Jan Burton, Steve Gorton, David Johnson,
Dave King, David Murray, Stephen Oliver, Tim Ridley, Guy Ryecart,
Jules Selmes, Steve Shott, Colin Walton, and Alex Wilson

First published in Great Britain in 1998
by Dorling Kindersley Limited,
9 Henrietta Street, London WC2E 8PS

A CIP catalogue record for this book is available
from the British Library
ISBN 0-7513-0433-6

Reproduced in Italy by Colorlito Rigogliosi S.R.L., Milan
Printed and bound in Singapore by Tien Wah Press

CONTENTS

The Birth 4
The Naming Ceremony 6
The Family Tree 7

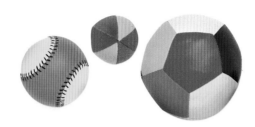

THE SECOND YEAR

THE THIRD YEAR

THE FOURTH YEAR

THE FIFTH YEAR

THE BIRTH

Date and time

Place

Weight and length

Colour of eyes

Colour of hair

Baby looks like . . .

Comments on the birth

HOSPITAL TAG

BIRTH ANNOUNCEMENT

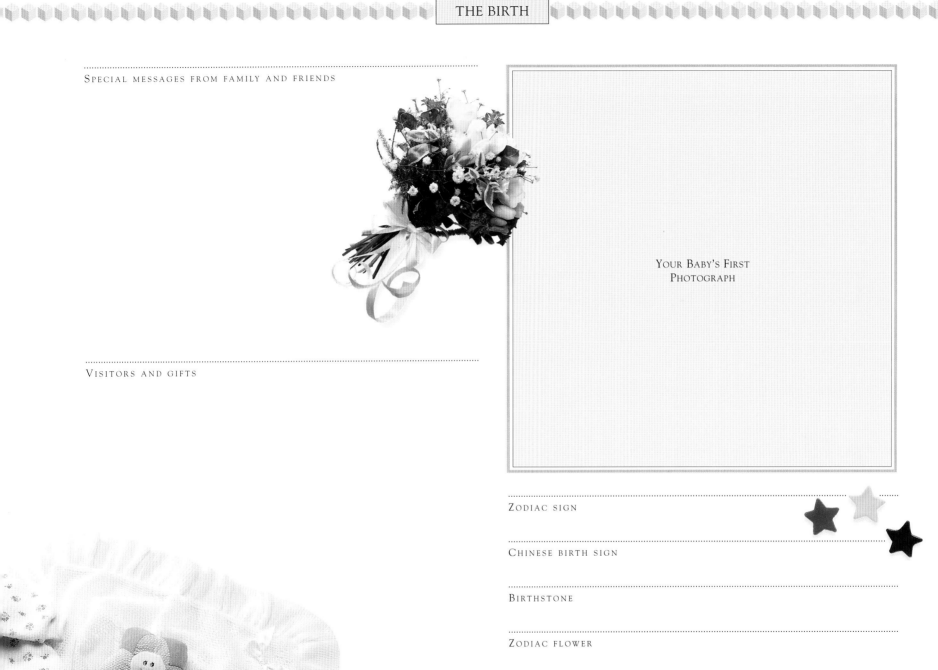

SPECIAL MESSAGES FROM FAMILY AND FRIENDS

VISITORS AND GIFTS

YOUR BABY'S FIRST
PHOTOGRAPH

ZODIAC SIGN

CHINESE BIRTH SIGN

BIRTHSTONE

ZODIAC FLOWER

THE NAMING CEREMONY

Your baby's full name
....

Reason for the choice of name
....

....

Date and time of the ceremony
....

Location of the ceremony
....

Your baby's outfit
....

Description of the ceremony

Guests present
....

Gifts received / from whom
....

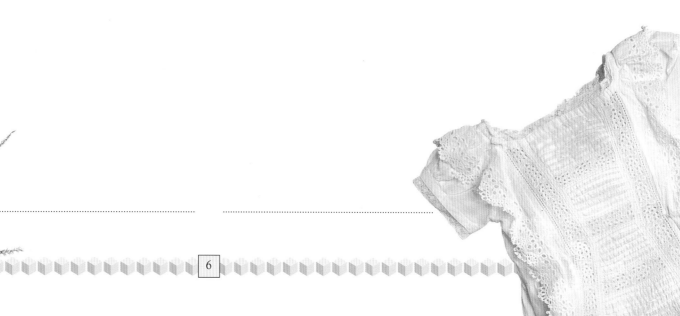

....

GRANDMOTHER
PHOTOGRAPH

GRANDFATHER
PHOTOGRAPH

GRANDMOTHER
PHOTOGRAPH

GRANDFATHER
PHOTOGRAPH

THE FAMILY TREE

MOTHER
PHOTOGRAPH

FATHER
PHOTOGRAPH

BROTHERS AND SISTERS
PHOTOGRAPH

BABY
PHOTOGRAPH

BROTHERS AND SISTERS
PHOTOGRAPH

THE FIRST YEAR

DURING THE FIRST FEW WEEKS of life your baby has to adjust to surviving outside the womb. At this time his needs are very basic: he feeds, cries, and sleeps for much of the time. As your baby matures, he begins to develop an interest in the surrounding world, to react to different stimuli, and to want to explore his immediate environment.

Your baby learns through his senses and by using his body. Anything that is not within his range of vision, smell, or touch does not exist for him. He will discover his body by moving his limbs constantly, kicking his legs rhythmically, and waving his arms about. A very young baby is limited in his ability to communicate his feelings, and initially can only cry when distressed. In the course of his first year, however, your baby will begin to make a wide variety of cooing and babbling sounds, and towards the end of the year may articulate the beginning of an identifiable word. At this stage of life a baby's parent or principal carer is the centre of his world, and he relies on her constant presence for his well being. He can easily recognize her face, and is comforted by her voice.

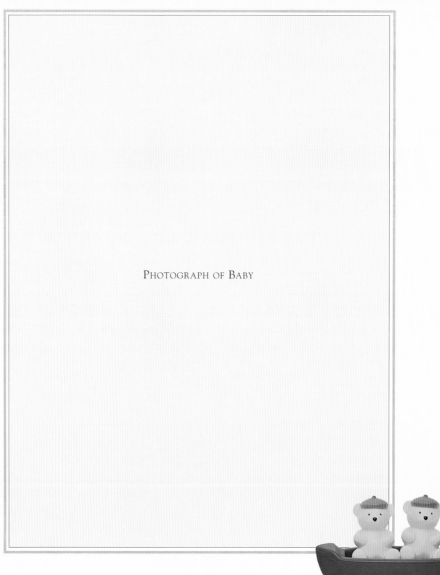

PHOTOGRAPH OF BABY

MEMORABLE MILESTONES

FIRST SMILES

....

FIRST HOLDS HEAD UP

....

FIRST HOLDS OBJECT IN HANDS

....

GROWS FIRST TOOTH

....

FIRST PICKS UP OBJECT WITH FINGER AND THUMB

....

FIRST SLEEPS THROUGH THE NIGHT

....

FIRST EATS UNAIDED

....

FIRST ROLLS OVER

....

FIRST SITS UP UNAIDED

....

FIRST CRAWLS

....

FIRST STANDS UNAIDED

....

TAKES FIRST STEPS

....

UTTERS FIRST WORD

....

FIRST USES A WORD FOR FATHER OR MOTHER

....

TREASURED MOMENTS

PERSONALITY

THINGS THAT MAKE YOUR BABY . . .

SMILE OR LAUGH

CALM AND SETTLED

EXCITED

UPSET

PHOTOGRAPH

SLEEP PATTERNS

DESCRIPTION OF CHARACTER

FAVOURITE THINGS

FOOD

DRINK

CUDDLY TOYS

BATH TOYS

OTHER TOYS

ANIMALS

PHOTOGRAPH OF BEST FRIEND

SONGS AND LULLABIES

FAVOURITE ADULTS

SPECIAL FRIENDS

DAILY LIFE

MORNING

MIDDAY

AFTERNOON

BATH TIME

BEDTIME

FEEDING SCHEDULE

FAVOURITE TIME OF DAY

WORST TIME OF DAY

SPECIAL MOMENTS

HOLIDAYS AND OUTINGS

FIRST HOLIDAY

DATE
....

PLACE
....

THE JOURNEY
....

WHERE YOU STAYED
....
....

YOUR BABY'S BEHAVIOUR
....
....

AMUSING INCIDENTS
....
....

SPECIAL MEMORIES
....

HOLIDAY PHOTOGRAPH

MEMORABLE OUTINGS

VISITS TO RELATIVES AND FRIENDS
....
....

OTHER OUTINGS
....
....

FIRST CHRISTMAS

WHERE CHRISTMAS WAS SPENT

WHAT YOU DID ON CHRISTMAS EVE

WHAT YOU DID ON CHRISTMAS DAY

Photograph

YOUR PRESENTS TO YOUR BABY

OTHER GIFTS RECEIVED / FROM WHOM

WHAT YOUR BABY ATE

WHAT YOU DID ON BOXING DAY

WHAT TIME YOUR BABY WOKE UP

FIRST BIRTHDAY

PLACE AND TIME

....

FOOD AND DRINKS

....

THE CAKE

....

WHAT YOUR BABY WORE

....

OTHER CHILDREN PRESENT

....

ADULTS PRESENT

....

BIRTHDAY PHOTOGRAPH

GIFTS RECEIVED / FROM WHOM

....

MEMORABLE INCIDENTS

....

THE SECOND YEAR

YOUR ONE-YEAR-OLD wants to explore everything within reach, and tries to understand the world through these investigations. During her second year she will learn to walk, and become increasingly mobile and independent. She will enjoy all manner of physical games and activities, which will help her to develop good muscle tone and fine-tune her skills. At this stage your child has very little memory or ability for premeditated thought. Because she has very little common sense and invariably tends to repeat mistakes, you, or another adult, need to keep an eye on her at all times. Your child needs to feel secure, and relies upon her parents or other carers to act as her bedrock and interpreter of the world. Her ability to understand what people are saying will increase dramatically during this second year, although she will comprehend a great deal more than she is able to express verbally. At this time, she will also begin to imitate adults, copying things that she experiences or sees, and helping her parents as they go about their daily tasks. Your child also enjoys being with her peers, but she does not, as yet, interact with them directly.

PHOTOGRAPH OF CHILD

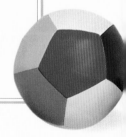

MEMORABLE MILESTONES

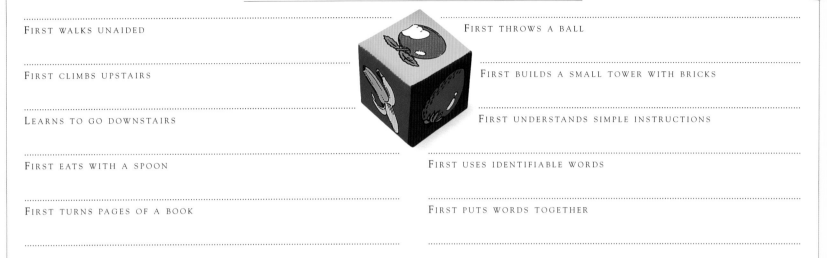

FIRST WALKS UNAIDED

FIRST THROWS A BALL

FIRST CLIMBS UPSTAIRS

FIRST BUILDS A SMALL TOWER WITH BRICKS

LEARNS TO GO DOWNSTAIRS

FIRST UNDERSTANDS SIMPLE INSTRUCTIONS

FIRST EATS WITH A SPOON

FIRST USES IDENTIFIABLE WORDS

FIRST TURNS PAGES OF A BOOK

FIRST PUTS WORDS TOGETHER

TREASURED MOMENTS

PERSONALITY

PHOTOGRAPH

YOUR CHILD'S VOCABULARY

MISPRONUNCIATIONS OF WORDS

WORDS FOR ANIMALS

WORDS FOR PEOPLE

THINGS THAT MAKE YOUR CHILD . . .

HAPPY OR AMUSED

EXCITED

HAVE A TANTRUM

FRIGHTENED OR NERVOUS

DESCRIPTION OF CHARACTER

FAVOURITE THINGS

FOOD

DRINK

TOYS AND GAMES

DOLL OR TEDDY

ANIMALS

SONGS AND RHYMES

BOOKS AND STORIES

CLOTHES

PHOTOGRAPH OF BEST FRIEND

FAVOURITE ADULTS

SPECIAL FRIENDS

DAILY LIFE

DAILY ROUTINE

MORNING

MIDDAY

AFTERNOON

BATH TIME

BEDTIME

FAVOURITE TIME OF DAY

WORST TIME OF DAY

SPECIAL MOMENTS

DESCRIPTION OF DAILY ACTIVITIES

PLAYING WITH FAVOURITE TOYS

DRAWING AND PAINTING

LOOKING AT BOOKS

PUZZLES AND GAMES

PLAYING WITH DOUGH AND WATER

"HELPING" YOU

BATH TIME AND WATER PLAY

FAVOURITE BATH TOYS

BATH TIME ACTIVITIES

PHOTOGRAPH OF BATH TIME

RESPONSE TO BEING BATHED

RESPONSE TO HAIR BEING WASHED

HOW YOUR CHILD PLAYS IN WATER

IN A PADDLING POOL

IN A SWIMMING POOL

HOLIDAYS AND OUTINGS

ANNUAL HOLIDAY

DATE

PLACE

THE JOURNEY

WHERE YOU STAYED

FAVOURITE ACTIVITIES

NEW EXPERIENCES

SPECIAL MEMORIES

MEMORABLE OUTINGS

VISITS TO RELATIVES AND FRIENDS

OUTINGS TO THE COUNTRYSIDE

OTHER OUTINGS

HOLIDAY PHOTOGRAPHS

SECOND CHRISTMAS

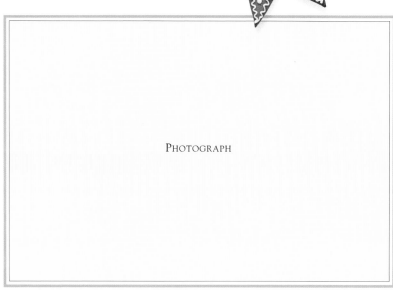

WHERE CHRISTMAS WAS SPENT

WHAT YOU DID ON CHRISTMAS EVE

WHAT YOU DID ON CHRISTMAS DAY

PHOTOGRAPH

OTHER GIFTS RECEIVED / FROM WHOM

WHAT YOUR CHILD ATE

YOUR PRESENTS TO YOUR CHILD

WHAT YOU DID ON BOXING DAY

SECOND BIRTHDAY

PLACE AND TIME

ENTERTAINMENT AND GAMES PLAYED

THE MOST POPULAR FOOD

THE CAKE

BIRTHDAY PHOTOGRAPH

OTHER CHILDREN PRESENT

GIFTS RECEIVED / FROM WHOM

ADULTS PRESENT

MEMORABLE INCIDENTS

THE THIRD YEAR

A TWO-YEAR-OLD CHILD has an insatiable curiosity about the world, and finds it endlessly fascinating. Your child will learn by assimilation and imitation, particularly through watching people going about their daily lives. Once he can talk he will ask questions constantly, and he will need to be introduced to new skills and activities so that he can broaden and enrich his experiences. Although the third year may sometimes be accompanied by tantrums, by the end of this year your child will become less self-centred. He will begin to be more accommodating towards others, and will make some attempt to develop the art of pleasing them. Physically, your child is becoming more competent and coordinated, and as his linguistic skills improve, so does his ability to express himself. At this stage of his development, your child views the world as a very physical place, and needs to be shown how to do things by being given practical demonstrations, rather than verbal explanations. At the beginning of this year, rather than play with other children directly, he will play alongside them in "parallel play", but as he reaches his third birthday, he will begin to enjoy the company of other children more and to participate in a variety of shared activities.

PHOTOGRAPH OF CHILD

MEMORABLE MILESTONES

FIRST DRINKS FROM A CUP WITHOUT A LID
....

FIRST SLEEPS IN A BED
....

FIRST SITS IN A NORMAL CHAIR
....

FIRST RIDES A TRICYCLE
....

FIRST WASHES FACE
....

FIRST CATCHES A BALL
....

FIRST BRUSHES TEETH
....

FIRST NAMES A COLOUR
....

FIRST GOES ALL DAY WITHOUT A NAPPY
....

FIRST BEGINS TO COUNT
....

FIRST TRIES TO GET DRESSED
....

FIRST RECITES A NURSERY RHYME
....

TREASURED MOMENTS

....

PERSONALITY

THINGS THAT MAKE YOUR CHILD . . .

HAPPY

AMUSED

EXCITED

HAVE A TANTRUM

FRIGHTENED OR NERVOUS

DESCRIPTION OF CHARACTER

PHOTOGRAPH

YOUR CHILD'S VOCABULARY

MISPRONUNCIATIONS OF WORDS

WORDS FOR ANIMALS AND PEOPLE

FAVOURITE THINGS

FOOD

DRINK

TOYS AND GAMES

DOLL OR TEDDY

ANIMALS

SONGS AND RHYMES

PHOTOGRAPH OF
BEST FRIEND

BOOKS AND STORIES

TELEVISION CHARACTERS

CLOTHES

FAVOURITE ADULTS

SPECIAL FRIENDS

DAILY LIFE

DAILY ROUTINE

MORNING

MIDDAY

AFTERNOON

BATH TIME

BEDTIME

FAVOURITE TIME OF DAY

WORST TIME OF DAY

DESCRIPTION OF DAILY ACTIVITIES

DRAWING AND PAINTING

MAKING THINGS

PLAYING WITH DOUGH AND CLAY

OUTDOOR GAMES

"HELPING" YOU

NURSERY SCHOOL

Name and address of the nursery school

....

....

Date of the first day

....

Names of the teachers and helpers

....

....

Your feelings about the first day

....

....

Your child's reaction to the first day

....

....

How quickly your child settled

....

....

Your child's favourite activities

....

....

PHOTOGRAPH OF YOUR CHILD
GOING TO NURSERY SCHOOL

HOLIDAYS AND OUTINGS

ANNUAL HOLIDAY

DATE

PLACE

THE JOURNEY

WHERE YOU STAYED

FAVOURITE ACTIVITIES

NEW EXPERIENCES

SPECIAL MEMORIES

MEMORABLE OUTINGS

VISITS TO RELATIVES AND FRIENDS

OUTINGS TO THE COUNTRYSIDE

OTHER OUTINGS

HOLIDAY PHOTOGRAPHS

THIRD CHRISTMAS

WHERE CHRISTMAS WAS SPENT

WHAT YOU DID ON CHRISTMAS EVE

PHOTOGRAPH

YOUR PRESENTS TO YOUR CHILD

OTHER GIFTS RECEIVED / FROM WHOM

WHAT YOU DID ON CHRISTMAS DAY

WHAT YOU DID ON BOXING DAY

WHO WAS THERE

THIRD BIRTHDAY

PLACE AND TIME

ENTERTAINMENT AND GAMES PLAYED

BIRTHDAY PHOTOGRAPH

THE MOST POPULAR FOOD

THE CAKE

OTHER CHILDREN PRESENT

ADULTS PRESENT

GIFTS RECEIVED / FROM WHOM

MEMORABLE INCIDENTS

THE FOURTH YEAR

DURING HER FOURTH YEAR, your child begins to understand the concept of time and to grasp the idea of past and future, yesterday and tomorrow. She will develop an understanding of cause and effect, and the realization that she cannot always have what she wants when she wants it. She begins to establish her own moral code: the concepts of "right" and "wrong" begin to take on meaning, and her consideration for others increases. She will start to offer instead of always taking, and will learn to befriend other children, share with them, take turns, and make compromises. As your child's skills develop, she is able to exert more control over her world, and gains confidence in her abilities. Her manual dexterity increases and she is able to carry out a wide range of tasks. She will start to show an interest in writing and will concentrate for longer when listening to a story.

By her fourth year, she will also be calmer and less prone to tantrums. Understanding everything she sees around her becomes very important, and she continues to act out real-life situations in imaginative play.

PHOTOGRAPH OF CHILD

MEMORABLE MILESTONES

FIRST EATS WITH A KNIFE AND FORK

FIRST DRAWS A RECOGNIZABLE FIGURE

FIRST COUNTS UP TO TWENTY AND FORMS LETTERS

FIRST COMPLETES A SIMPLE JIGSAW

FIRST DRESSES HERSELF PROPERLY

FIRST HOPS ON ONE FOOT

FIRST SKIPS

FIRST SHARES A TOY

TREASURED MOMENTS

PERSONALITY

PHOTOGRAPH

DESCRIPTION OF CHARACTER

THINGS THAT MAKE YOUR CHILD . . .

HAPPY

LAUGH

EXCITED

CALM

THOUGHTFUL

ANGRY

INSECURE

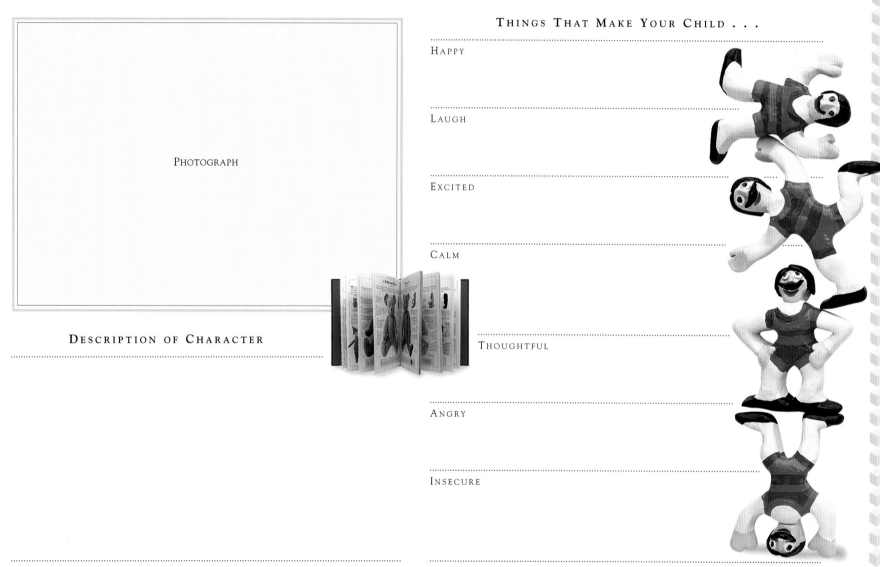

FAVOURITE THINGS

FOOD

DRINK

TOYS

BOOKS AND STORIES

PHOTOGRAPH OF
BEST FRIEND

TELEVISION CHARACTERS

ANIMALS

CLOTHES

SONGS AND RHYMES

FAVOURITE ADULTS

SPORTS AND GAMES

SPECIAL FRIENDS

DAILY LIFE

DAILY ROUTINE

MORNING

MIDDAY

AFTERNOON

BATH TIME

BEDTIME

WEEKLY ACTIVITIES

CLUBS AND CLASSES ATTENDED BY YOUR CHILD

DESCRIPTION OF DAILY ACTIVITIES

DRAWING AND PAINTING

MAKING THINGS

PLAYING WITH DOUGH AND CLAY

OUTDOOR GAMES

"HELPING" YOU

DRESSING UP

OTHER ACTIVITIES

HOLIDAYS AND OUTINGS

ANNUAL HOLIDAY

DATE ....

PLACE ....

THE JOURNEY

....

WHERE YOU STAYED

....

FAVOURITE ACTIVITIES

....

AMUSING INCIDENTS

....

SPECIAL MEMORIES

....

HOLIDAY PHOTOGRAPH

MEMORABLE OUTINGS

VISITS TO RELATIVES AND FRIENDS

....

OTHER OUTINGS

....

FOURTH CHRISTMAS

WHERE CHRISTMAS WAS SPENT

WHAT YOU DID ON CHRISTMAS EVE

WHAT YOU DID ON CHRISTMAS DAY

PHOTOGRAPH

YOUR PRESENTS TO YOUR CHILD

OTHER GIFTS RECEIVED / FROM WHOM

WHO WAS THERE

WHAT YOU DID ON BOXING DAY

FOURTH BIRTHDAY

PLACE AND TIME

ENTERTAINMENT AND GAMES PLAYED

THE MOST POPULAR FOOD

THE CAKE

OTHER CHILDREN PRESENT

ADULTS PRESENT

BIRTHDAY PHOTOGRAPH

GIFTS RECEIVED / FROM WHOM

MEMORABLE INCIDENTS

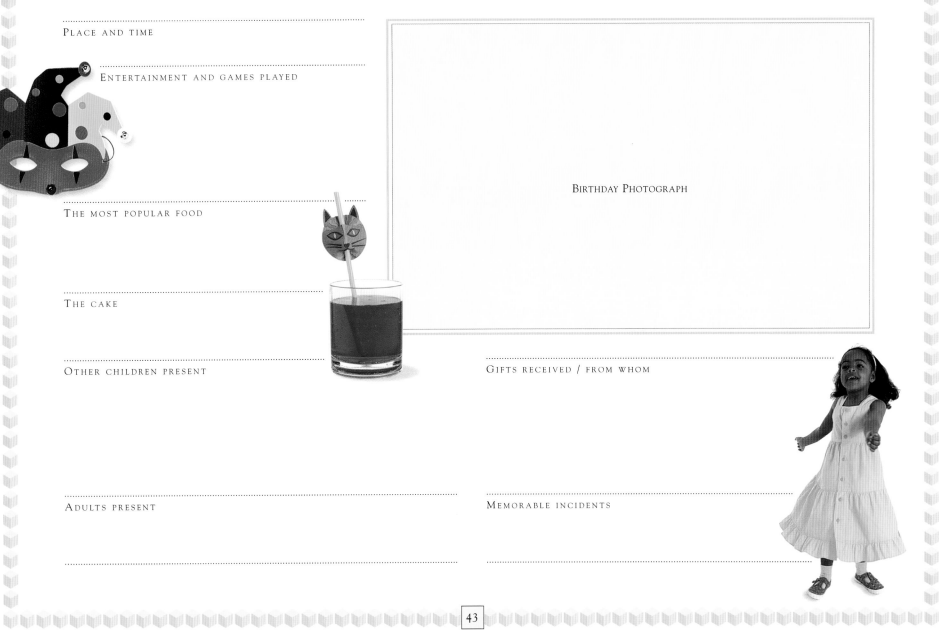

THE FIFTH YEAR

BY THE FIFTH YEAR, your child is very able physically, and can run, jump, hop, skip, and climb with ease. Body and emotions remain closely related, and your child frequently articulates his feelings in a physical way – for example, he may jump in the air for joy, or stamp his feet in anger. At this age a child likes the world to be well structured, and may derive great satisfaction and enjoyment from categorizing and ordering things. Your child's vocabulary continues to expand, and with it the ability to express himself. He often asks pertinent and searching questions about the world around him, and may wonder about other profound issues, such as death and sex. Although your child's imagination continues to mature, he is very literal in his comprehension of things, and remains highly impressionable. He becomes less dependent on his parents and relishes the company of other children. He enjoys playing with them and begins to form proper friendships. This is the time when he starts to learn to exist in a wider world without his mother or father, and to enjoy the social experience of becoming part of a group.

PHOTOGRAPH OF CHILD

MEMORABLE MILESTONES

FIRST READS A WORD

FIRST RECITES OWN ADDRESS

FIRST WRITES OWN NAME

FIRST TELLS A JOKE

FIRST SWIMS UNAIDED

FIRST TIES OWN SHOELACES

FIRST RIDES A BICYCLE WITH STABILIZERS

FIRST TELLS THE TIME

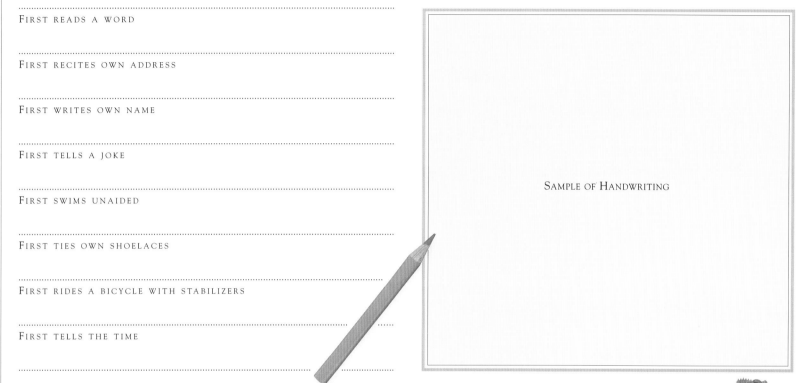

SAMPLE OF HANDWRITING

TREASURED MOMENTS

PERSONALITY

PHOTOGRAPH OR
HAND PRINT

DESCRIPTION OF CHARACTER

THINGS THAT MAKE YOUR CHILD . . .

HAPPY

LAUGH

EXCITED

CALM

THOUGHTFUL

ANGRY

INSECURE

FAVOURITE THINGS

FOOD

DRINK

TOYS

ANIMALS

PHOTOGRAPH OF
BEST FRIEND

BOOKS AND STORIES

TELEVISION CHARACTERS

CLOTHES

SONGS AND RHYMES

SPORTS AND GAMES

FAVOURITE ADULTS

SPECIAL FRIENDS

DAILY LIFE

DAILY ROUTINE

MORNING

MIDDAY

AFTERNOON

BATH TIME

BEDTIME

WEEKLY ACTIVITIES

CLUBS AND CLASSES ATTENDED BY YOUR CHILD

DESCRIPTION OF DAILY ACTIVITIES

DRAWING AND PAINTING

MAKING THINGS

PLAYING WITH DOUGH AND CLAY

OUTDOOR GAMES

"HELPING" YOU

DRESSING UP

OTHER ACTIVITIES

FIRST DAYS AT SCHOOL

NAME AND ADDRESS OF THE SCHOOL
....

....

DATE OF THE FIRST DAY
....

NAME OF THE TEACHER
....

NAME OF THE HEAD TEACHER
....

DIARY OF THE SCHOOL DAY
....

....

PHOTOGRAPH OF YOUR CHILD
GOING TO SCHOOL

....
FAVOURITE CLASSROOM ACTIVITIES

....

YOUR FEELINGS ABOUT THE FIRST DAY

....

....
YOUR CHILD'S COMMENTS ON THE DAY

....

....
NAMES OF OTHER CHILDREN

....

HOLIDAYS AND OUTINGS

ANNUAL HOLIDAY

DATE

PLACE

THE JOURNEY

WHERE YOU STAYED

FAVOURITE ACTIVITIES

AMUSING INCIDENTS

SPECIAL MEMORIES

MEMORABLE OUTINGS

VISITS TO RELATIVES AND FRIENDS

OUTINGS TO THE COUNTRYSIDE

OTHER OUTINGS

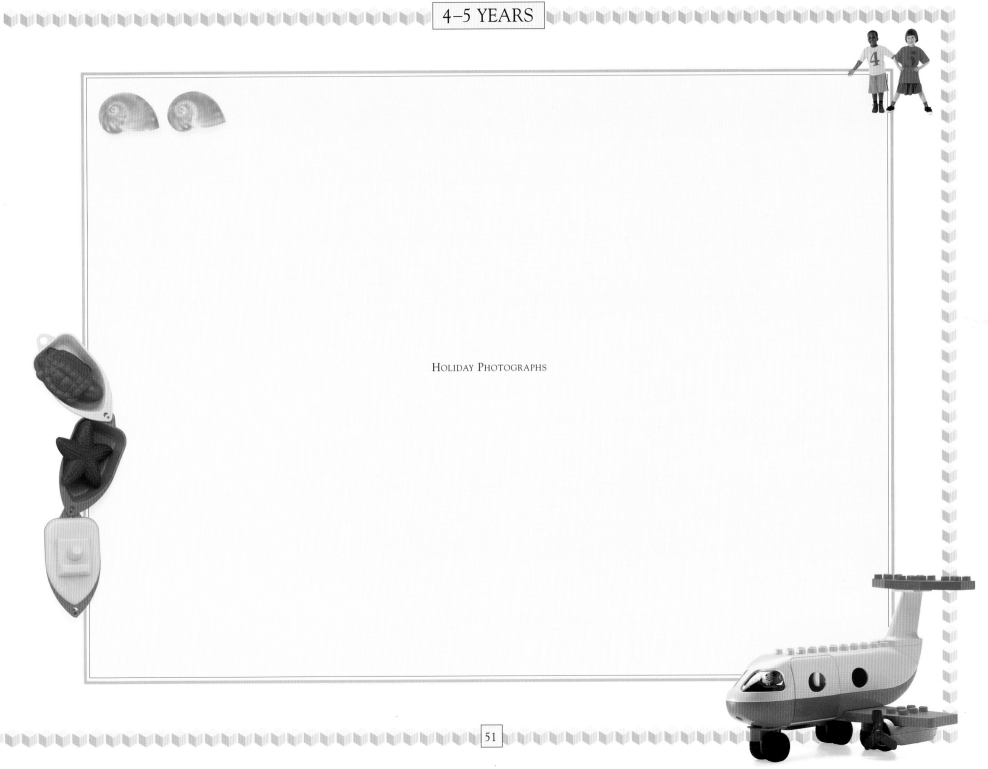

HOLIDAY PHOTOGRAPHS

FIFTH CHRISTMAS

WHERE CHRISTMAS WAS SPENT

WHAT YOU DID ON CHRISTMAS EVE

PHOTOGRAPH

WHAT YOU DID ON CHRISTMAS DAY

OTHER GIFTS RECEIVED / FROM WHOM

WHO WAS THERE

WHAT YOU DID ON BOXING DAY

YOUR PRESENTS TO YOUR CHILD

FIFTH BIRTHDAY

PLACE AND TIME

ENTERTAINMENT AND GAMES PLAYED

THE MOST POPULAR FOOD

THE CAKE

OTHER CHILDREN PRESENT

BIRTHDAY PHOTOGRAPH

ADULTS PRESENT

GIFTS RECEIVED / FROM WHOM

MEMORABLE INCIDENTS

PHYSICAL RECORD

AGE	HEIGHT	WEIGHT	CLOTHES SIZE	SHOE SIZE
SIX MONTHS				
ONE YEAR				
EIGHTEEN MONTHS				
TWO YEARS				
TWO AND A HALF YEARS				
THREE YEARS				
THREE AND A HALF YEARS				
FOUR YEARS				
FOUR AND A HALF YEARS				
FIVE YEARS				
NOTES				

HEIGHT

Draw your child's height and weight on these graphs at six-monthly intervals. Use metric or imperial measurements, but do not mix them.

WEIGHT

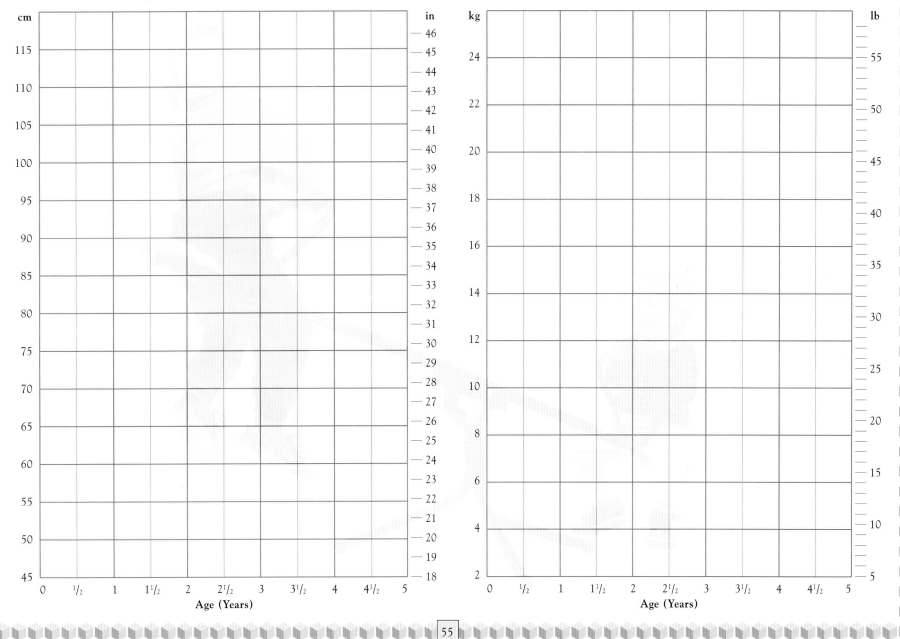

MEDICAL RECORD

TEETHING

	Age	Date
FIRST TOOTH		
SECOND TOOTH		
THIRD TOOTH		
FOURTH TOOTH		
FIFTH TOOTH		
SIXTH TOOTH		
SEVENTH TOOTH		
EIGHTH TOOTH		
NINTH TOOTH		
TENTH TOOTH		

IMMUNIZATIONS

Vaccine	Age	Date
DIPHTHERIA/TETANUS/ WHOOPING COUGH (DTP)		
POLIO (OPV)		
HAEMOPHILUS INFLUENZAE TYPE B (HIB)		
MEASLES/MUMPS/ RUBELLA (MMR)		
OTHER VACCINES		

TESTS

Test	Age	Date
HEARING		
EYESIGHT		
GENERAL MEDICAL		

CHILDHOOD ILLNESSES

Diagnosis	Age	Date

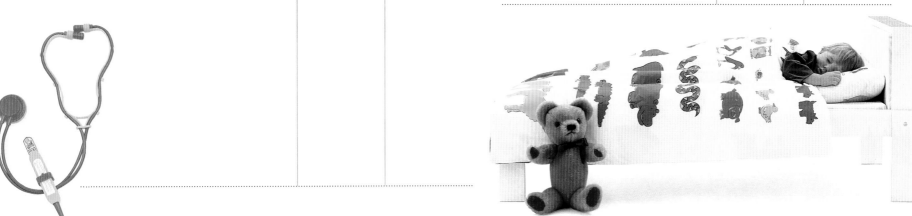